The Easy Ke...

Shirley Bassey

15 classic songs for keyboard

Published 2001

Series Editor Anna Joyce
Design & Art Direction Dominic Brookman

Music arranged & processed by Barnes Music Engraving Ltd East Sussex TN34 1HA
Cover Image Redferns Picture Library

© International Music Publications Ltd
Griffin House 161 Hammersmith Road London England W6 8BS

(aunt strictly!)

FROM "OLIVER"

As Long As He Needs Me

Words and Music by Lionel Bart

Suggested Registration: Electric Piano
Rhythm: Rhumba
Tempo: ♩ = 76

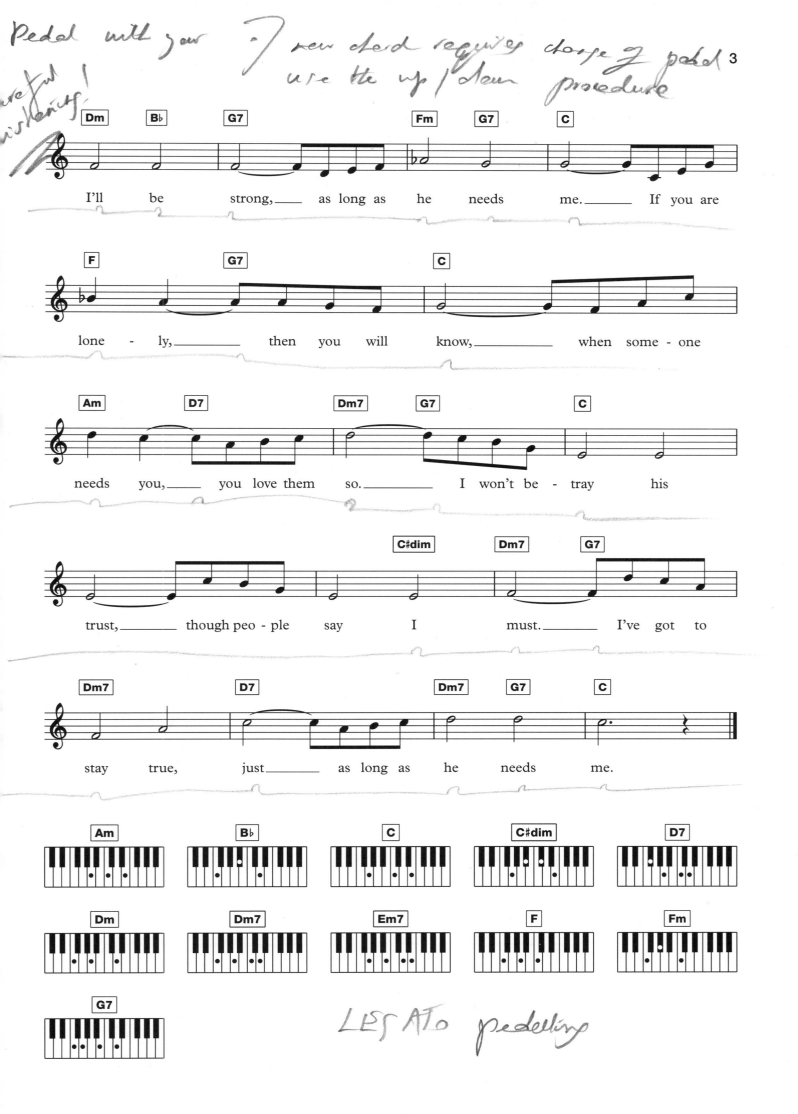

Big Spender

Words by Dorothy Fields / Music by Cy Coleman

Suggested Registration: Brass
Rhythm: Jazz Swing
Tempo: ♩ = 116

DIAMONDS ARE FOREVER

Words by Don Black / Music by John Barry

Suggested Registration: Pop Organ / Synth
Rhythm: 8 Beat
Tempo: ♩ = 105

Goldfinger

Words by Anthony Newley and Leslie Bricusse / Music by John Barry

Suggested Registration: Brass / Pop Organ
Rhythm: 8 Beat
Tempo: ♩ = 105

THE GREATEST PERFORMANCE OF MY LIFE

Words and Music by Oscar Anderle and Sandro / English Words by Robert Allen

Suggested Registration: Saxophone / Strings
Rhythm: 8 Beat
Tempo: ♩ = 76

Memory Lane Music Ltd, London WC2H 8NA

If You Go Away
(Ne Me Quitte Pas)

Words by Rod McKuen / Music by Jacques Brel

Suggested Registration: Oboe / Strings
Rhythm: Waltz
Tempo: ♩ = 80

If you go a - way, on this sum-mer day, then you might as well take the sun a -

- way, all the birds that flew in the sum-mer sky when our love was new, and our hearts were

high, when the day was young, and the night was long, and the moon stood still for the night-bird's

song, if you go a - way, if you go a - way, if you go a - way, if you go a - way. But if you

stay, I'll make you a day, like no day has been, or will be a - gain, we'll sail the sun, we'll ride on the

rain, we'll talk to the trees, and wor-ship the wind. Then if you go, I'll un-der-stand, leave me just e -

- nough love to fill up my hand. If you go a - way,   if you go a - way,   if you go a - way,   if you go a -

- way. _____   If you go a - way, as I know you will, you must tell the world to stop turn-ing

till, you re-turn a - gain, if you ev - er   do,   for what good is   love with-out lov-ing

you? Can I tell you now, as you turn to   go,   I'll be dy-ing   slow-ly till the next hel -

- lo?   If you go a - way,   if you go a - way,   if you go a - way, please don't go a - way.

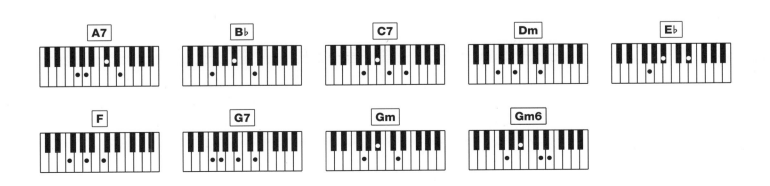

Kiss Me, Honey Honey, Kiss Me

Words and Music by Albon Timothy and Michael Julien

Suggested Registration: Brass
Rhythm: Cha Cha
Tempo: ♩ = 124

Kiss me, ho-ney, ho-ney, kiss me. Thrill me, ho-ney, ho-ney,

thrill me. Don't care ev-en if I blow my top___ but ho-ney,

ho-ney, (mm,)___ don't stop! I'd like to play a lit-tle

game with you,___ a lit-tle game es-pe-cially made for two.___

If you come close then I will show you how, clo-ser, clo-ser, now.

Kiss me, ho-ney, ho-ney, kiss me. Thrill me, ho-ney, ho-ney, thrill me.

Don't care ev-en if I blow my top__ but ho-ney, ho-ney, (mm,)__ don't stop.

Don't care ev-en if I blow my top__ but ho-ney, ho-ney,

don't stop.

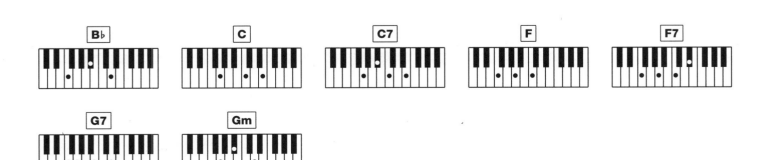

The Lady Is A Tramp

Words by Lorenz Hart / Music by Richard Rodgers

Suggested Registration: Saxophone
Rhythm: Swing
Tempo: ♩ = 132

I get too hun-gry for din-ner at eight,___

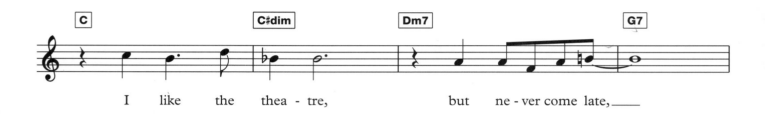

I like the thea-tre, but ne-ver come late,___

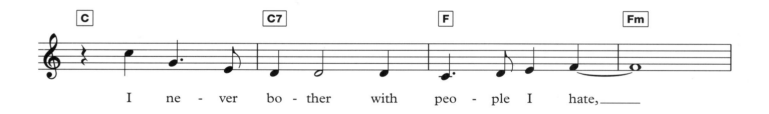

I ne-ver bo-ther with peo-ple I hate,___

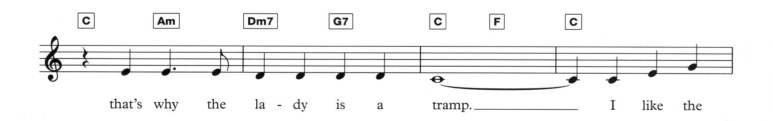

that's why the la-dy is a tramp.___ I like the

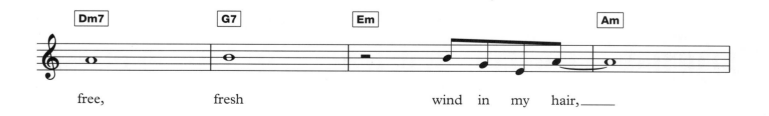

free, fresh wind in my hair,___

life with-out care,___ I'm broke, it's oke,

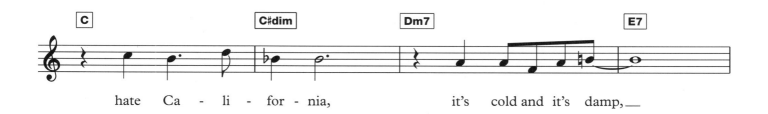

hate Ca - li - for - nia, it's cold and it's damp, __

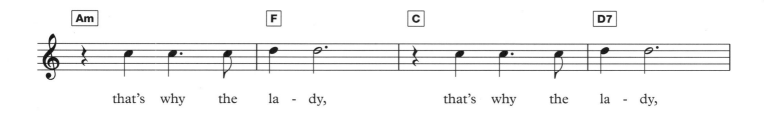

that's why the la - dy, that's why the la - dy,

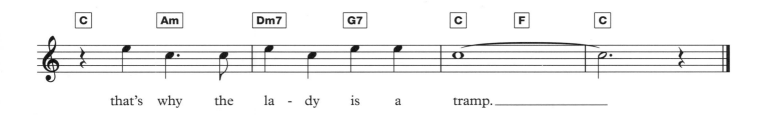

that's why the la - dy is a tramp._____

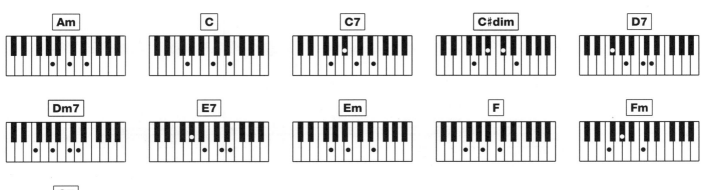

Moonraker

Words by Don Black / Music by John Barry

Suggested Registration: Electric Piano / Strings
Rhythm: Bossa Nova
Tempo: ♩ = 110

Where are you?_____ Why do you hide?

Where is that moon - light trail that leads____ to your side?____

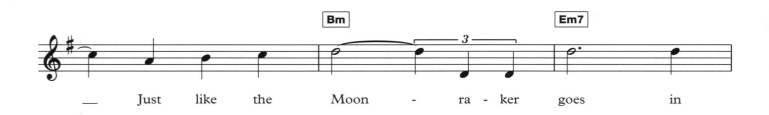

__ Just like the Moon - ra - ker goes in

search_____ of his dream of gold, I_____ search for

love, for some - one to have and hold. I've

seen   your   smile_____   in   a   thou - sand   dreams,

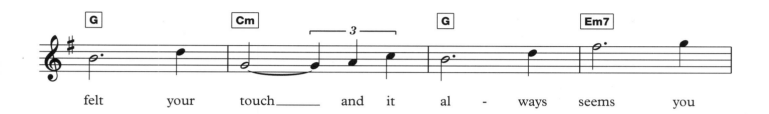

felt   your   touch_____   and   it   al - ways   seems   you

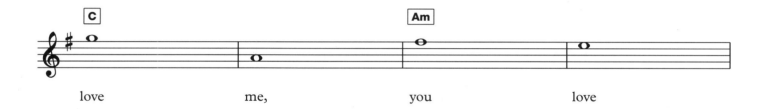

love   me,   you   love

me.

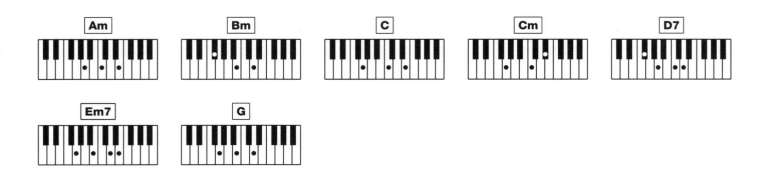

SOMETHING

Words and Music by George Harrison

Suggested Registration: Vibraphone / Flute
Rhythm: 16 Beat
Tempo: ♩ = 76

Some-thing in the way he moves, at-tracts me like no oth-er

lov - er._____ Some-thing in the way he woos me,_____ I

don't want to leave him now, you know I be-lieve and how._

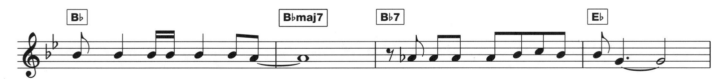

Some-where in his smile he knows,__ that I don't need no oth-er lov-er.____

Some-thing in his style that shows me,_____ I don't want to leave him now, you

know I be-lieve and how. __

21

THIS IS MY LIFE

Words by Norman Newell / Music by Bruno Canfora and Antonio Amurri

Suggested Registration: Guitar / Piano
Rhythm: Beguine
Tempo: ♩ = 96

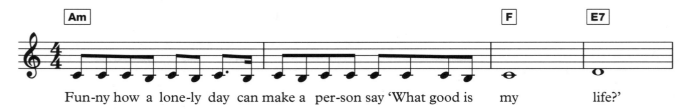

Fun-ny how a lone-ly day can make a per-son say 'What good is my life?'

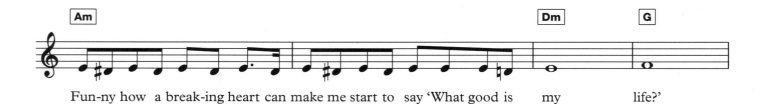

Fun-ny how a break-ing heart can make me start to say 'What good is my life?'

Fun-ny how I of-ten seem to think I'll find a-no-ther dream in my life.

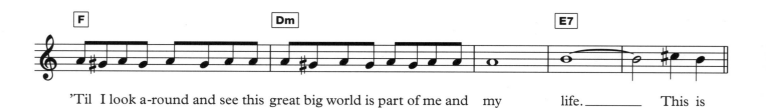

'Til I look a-round and see this great big world is part of me and my life._____ This is

my life,___ to-day, to-mor-row lost, but come and find me. For

WHAT KIND OF FOOL AM I?

Words and Music by Leslie Bricusse and Anthony Newley

Suggested Registration: Piano / Strings
Rhythm: Swing
Tempo: ♩ = 110

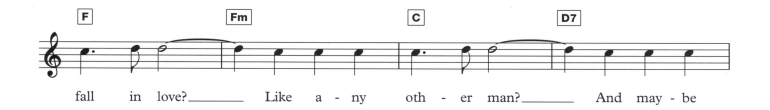

fall in love?_____ Like a - ny oth - er man?_____ And may - be

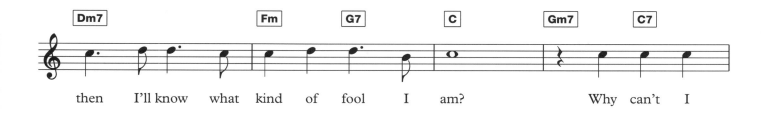

then I'll know what kind of fool I am? Why can't I

fall in love? 'Til I don't give a damn. And may - be

then I'll know what kind of fool I am.

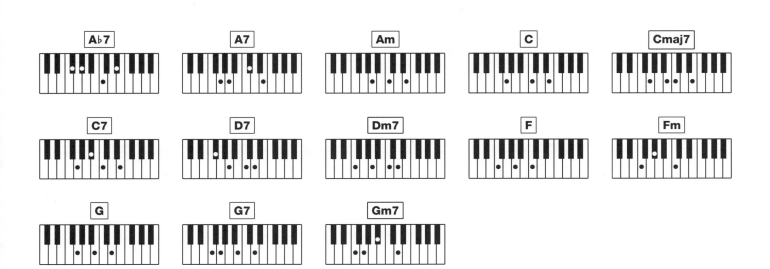

What Now My Love?

Original Words by Pierre Delanoe / Music by Gilbert Becaud / English Words by Carl Sigman

Suggested Registration: Vibraphone / Strings
Rhythm: 16 Beat
Tempo: ♩ = 103

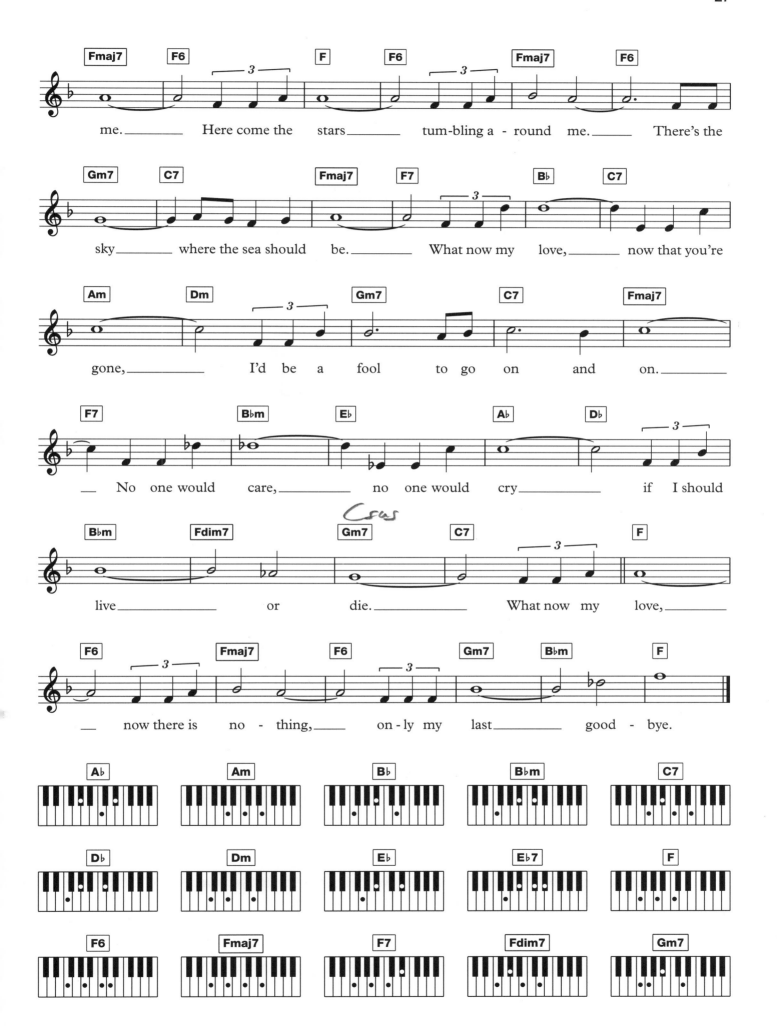

WHERE DO I BEGIN?

Words by Carl Sigman / Music by Francis Lai

Suggested Registration: Strings
Rhythm: 8 Beat
Tempo: ♩ = 88

Where do I be-gin   to tell the sto-ry of how great a love can be,

the sweet love sto-ry that is   old-er than the sea,   the sim-ple truth a-bout the

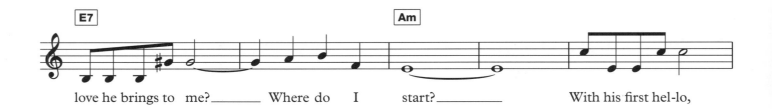

love he brings to me?_____ Where do I   start?_____   With his first hel-lo,

he gave a mean-ing to this   emp-ty world of mine,   there'd ne-ver be an-oth-er

love, an-oth-er time,   he came in-to my life and made the liv-ing fine._____

_ He fills my   heart,_____ he fills my   heart_ with ve-ry spe-cial things, with an-gel

You'll Never Know
(Just How Much I Love You)

Words by Mack Gordon / Music by Harry Warren

Suggested Registration: Saxophone / Strings
Rhythm: Bossa Nova
Tempo: ♩ = 100

Dar-ling I'm so blue with - out you,___ I think a - bout you,___ the live long day.

When you ask me if I'm lone - ly,___ then I have on - ly this to say.

You'll ne - ver know just how much I miss you,_____

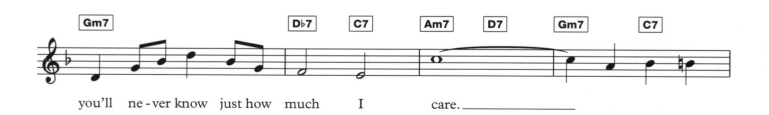

you'll ne - ver know just how much I care._____

And if I tried, I still could-n't hide my love for you.

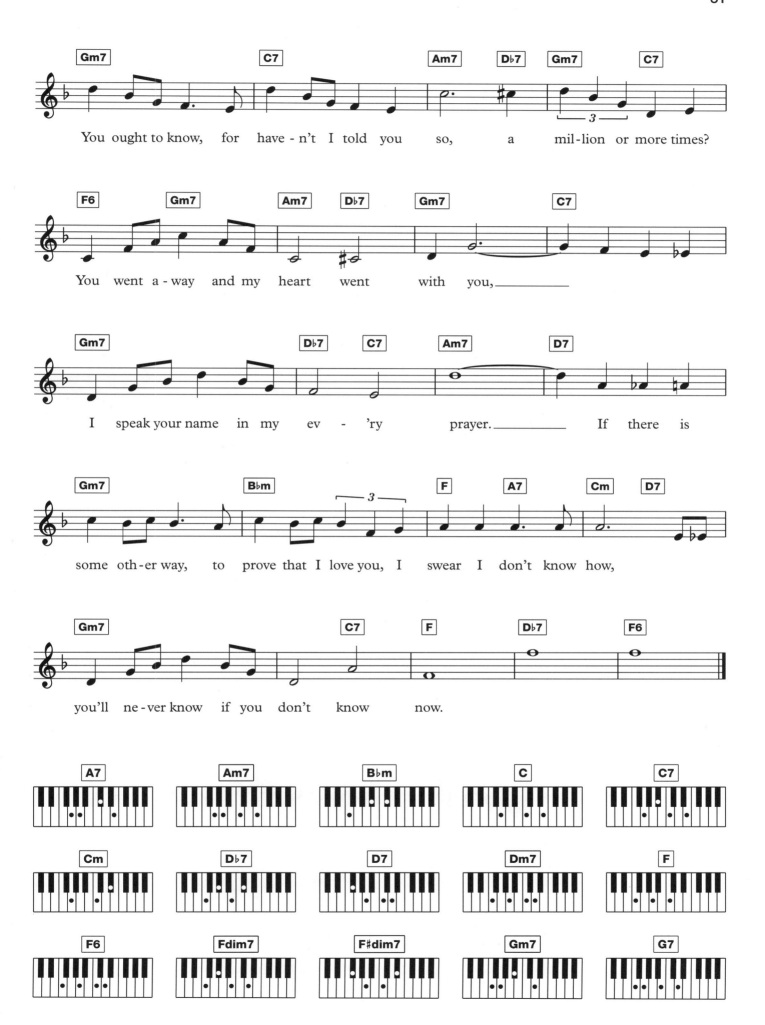

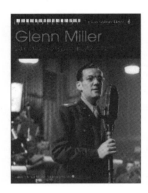